Rickety
Rocket

'**Rickety Rocket**'

An original concept by Alice Hemming

© Alice Hemming

Illustrated by Emma Randall

Published by MAVERICK ARTS PUBLISHING LTD

Studio 3A, City Business Centre, 6 Brighton Road,

Horsham, West Sussex, RH13 5BB

© Maverick Arts Publishing Limited November 2018

+44 (0)1403 256941

A CIP catalogue record for this book is available at the British Library.

ISBN 978-1-84886-393-4

www.maverickbooks.co.uk

This book is rated as: White Band (Guided Reading)

Rickety Rocket

By **Alice Hemming**

Illustrated by **Emma Randall**

Chapter 1

"Look at these beauties," said Stacey, flicking through her latest copy of Space Rockets Weekly.

She stood with her best friends in the Space Place café, jostling to look at the magazine.

"Which one do you like, Stacey?" asked Timble.

"Which colour would you get?" asked Moondoodle.

Stacey turned to her favourite page.

"This is the one," she said. "I'd buy this snazzy, purple, sporty rocket and I'd whiz off to Picnic Planet looking super-stylish. For once, I would be the one having fun, not serving other people drinks in the Space Place. But that's never going to happen – it's 999.99 space dollars."

Zip and Zap jumped up and down, pointing to a poster on the wall.

"Why don't you race in the Space Chase on Saturday?" asked Zip.

"1000 space dollars prize money. If you won, you could buy your favourite sporty rocket," said Zap.

Stacey sighed. "With my Rickety Rocket? I'd be lucky if I could get it off the ground."

Her friends looked at Stacey's squeaky, creaky, bashed and battered, old and rusty,

Rickety Rocket.

"Maybe it needs a bit of work," said Timble.

"Ha ha, it needs more than a bit of work!" boomed a voice. A tall boy in a shiny blue suit strode past, flashing a white smile.

"Astro Pete," muttered Moondoodle. "He's such a show-off."

Pete read the poster slowly, his smile spreading wider.

"Easy money!" he laughed.

"There's nobody out there who can beat me. You should leave the racing to the professionals, Stacey."

He kicked the Rickety Rocket and something inside went

CLUNK!

He strode away, still laughing.

"See?" said Stacey to her friends. "Everyone would laugh at me."

Timble climbed inside the rocket with his spanner. After a couple of minutes of banging and squeaking, his voice echoed out.

"The propelling nozzle is still working," he said.

"In English, please!" said Stacey.

"It means," said Timble, wheeling himself back out from the rocket, "that with a bit of work, the Rickety Rocket could fly in the Space Chase."

"I haven't got time to mend it," said Stacey, "I have to work in the café all week."

Zip and Zap glanced at each other. Zip looked at Moondoodle.

Zap winked at Timble. "We'll help!" they said. And they did.

Chapter 2

That week, while Stacey was wiping tables in the Space Place, she hardly saw her friends. Zip and Zap rushed in on Tuesday.

"Can we fill up our bucket of water?" asked Zip.

"And have you got any old rags?" said Zap.

Moondoodle dropped by on Wednesday with an old tin of purple paint.

"What do you think of this colour?" she said.

And Stacey didn't see Timble at all.

On Friday, Stacey didn't see her friends all day.
Jack Boom and Jill Zoom came by for their usual
milkshakes. They sat in the corner, whispering.
Stacey brought them their drinks.

"Is it true that you're entering the race tomorrow?" said Jack, sniggering.

"It might be," said Stacey. "Is there something funny about that?"

"No, not at all," said Jack, but as Stacey walked back to the counter, she heard their laughter getting louder.

Stacey sighed as she cleaned the counter. This was probably all a terrible idea. There was no way she was going to win a race against Jack, Jill and Pete. She would have to tell her friends that the whole thing was off.

But just as Stacey was closing up the Space

Place that evening, her four friends appeared at the door. They looked paint-splodged and tired but were all grinning widely.

"Come with us!" they said. "We've got a surprise for you."

They led her round to the rocket park behind the Space Place. A big white sheet was covering up something big.

"Ready?" asked Zap.

Stacey nodded.

"Ta-dah!" said Zip and he whipped off the sheet.

It was the Rickety Rocket. It looked very different to before.

"Wow," said Stacey. "It's, it's, it's..."

"Purple!" said Moondoodle. "I know it's your

favourite colour so I made sure I put it everywhere. I even covered the seats in purple flowery material – look."

"I hammered out the dents in the nose cone," said Timble. "It took ages but it's nearly straight."

"And we scrubbed and cleaned all the windows," said Zip and Zap. "You can see through them now."

Stacey looked at the rocket. It was still just as rickety but now it was a violent shade of violet – ten times worse than before. If she raced in this, the whole town would laugh at her.

Then she looked at her friends' faces. They had worked so hard all week.

"It's perfect," she said.

Chapter 3

On the day of the Space Chase, the racers lined up with their spectacular spacecraft.

Jack Boom buffed his super speedy GX77.

Jill Zoom polished her flashy, fast KP606.

Astro Pete patted his shiny shuttle.

And Spacey Stacey leaned glumly against the Rickety Rocket.

A crackly voice blared out from the loudspeaker.

 "All competitors get ready, the Great Space Chase is about to begin."

"Looks like this is it," said Stacey. "Wish me luck!"

"Don't go too fast," said Zip.

"Or too slow," said Zap.

"Keep your eye on Planet Pink," said Timble.

"And take my lucky moon rock," said Moondoodle.

The four friends raced over to join the watching crowds and Stacey climbed into the Rickety Rocket.

"Good luck everyone!" called Stacey to the other racers.

"You're the one who needs the luck," said Jack.

"You should stick to serving milkshakes," said Jill.

"You'll be behind me all the way!" said Pete.

Stacey didn't reply. She pushed her helmet onto her head, fastened her safety belt and gritted her teeth.

She was going to finish this race whatever they said.

The voice from the loudspeaker started up again:

"Welcome to the great Space Chase. One thousand space dollars will be awarded to the first person to reach Planet Pink and return to the starting point. Stand by for the countdown..."

As soon as the words were spoken, Pete's shiny shuttle shot off into the stars.

The GX77 and the KP606 were close behind.

Stacey tried to get the Rickety Rocket to start. Eventually it did blast off, and one of its boosters fell to the ground.

SMASH!

Despite the loud **CHUG, CHUG, CHUG** of the engine, Stacey was sure she could hear laughter from the crowds below.

Off she chugged, miles behind the others. Astro Pete was leading the way straight to Planet Pink. Jack Boom and Jill Zoom were fighting for second place.

One went right and the other went left. First it was Jack, and then it was Jill. They were so busy looking at each other that they forgot to look where they were going.

"They've taken their eyes off Planet Pink," said Stacey, to herself. "They're heading towards Planet Stink."

And it was true: the GX77 and the KP606 disappeared in completely the wrong direction.

Chapter 4

Stacey kept a nice straight line. "Not too fast," she said, "but not too slow. Maybe I need a bit more power."

The Rickety Rocket heaved and groaned and part of a wing broke off and whizzed into space.

CRACK!

SHWWEEEEEE!

Astro Pete zoomed easily around Planet Pink.
Stacey watched him heading back as she kept
going steadily forwards. As she rattled on, she
lost a fin, a door and part of the nose cone.

"Astro Pete might win but I am going to hold my
head up in second place," said Stacey, clutching
her lucky moon rock.

It looked like an easy victory for Astro Pete but as he hurtled towards the finish line, he looped the loop, waving to the crowds below.

"Look where you're going, Pete!" shouted Stacey, but of course he couldn't hear her.

And he couldn't see the large ball of rock heading in his direction.

"An asteroid!"

The shiny shuttle exploded in a glittering firework display.

Luckily Astro Pete pressed the eject button just

in time. He parachuted to safety looking very fed up.

Somehow, Spacey Stacey kept on going. She made a slow circle around the beautiful gas rings of Planet Pink and spluttered back in the direction she had come from.

CHUG! CHUG! CHUG!

There wasn't much left of the Rickety Rocket but there was enough to get her past the finish line. And this time, as she landed, she definitely heard the crowds.

Four familiar faces were the first ones to come
and congratulate her.

"What will you buy with the prize money,
Stacey?" asked Timble.

"Something fast?" said Zip.

"Something shiny?" said Zap.

"Something that will make everyone go WOW?" asked Moondoodle.

"You'll see," said Stacey.

☆ ☆ ☆

The following weekend, Stacey took the four friends back to the rocket park to see her new purchase.

"Ta-dah!" she said and Zip, Zap, Timble and Moondoodle were very surprised to see...

A squeaky, creaky, bashed and battered, old and rusty, rickety space bus.

"It's not snazzy," said Zip.

"Or sporty," said Zap.

"Or speedy," said Timble.

"It's not even purple!" said Moondoodle.

"I know," said Stacey, "but the most important thing is that it has enough room for all my friends. Now, who wants to go to Picnic Planet?"

The End

Book Bands for Guided Reading

The Institute of Education book banding system is a scale of colours that reflects the various levels of reading difficulty. The bands are assigned by taking into account the content, the language style, the layout and phonics. Word, phrase and sentence level work is also taken into consideration.

Maverick Early Readers are a bright, attractive range of books covering the pink to white bands. All of these books have been book banded for guided reading to the industry standard and edited by a leading educational consultant.

To view the whole Maverick Readers scheme, visit our website at

www.maverickearlyreaders.com

Or scan the QR code above to view our scheme instantly!